Understanding Maths

Key Stage 2

Problem Solving

Hilary Koll and Steve Mills

Name ______________________________

Schofield&Sims

Introduction

Problem solving is the process of applying your mathematical knowledge to solve everyday problems or puzzles. The first task is always to understand the information given in the problem, and then to decide what mathematics is needed to solve it. In this book you will learn different ways to approach a variety of problems, puzzles and patterns.

How to use this book

Before you start using this book, write your name in the name box on the first page.

Then decide how to begin. If you want a complete course on problem solving, you should work right through the book from beginning to end. Another way to use the book is to dip into it when you want to find out about a particular topic, such as ratio problems. The Contents page will help you to find the pages you need.

Whichever way you choose, don't try to do too much at once – it's better to work through the book in short bursts.

When you have found the topic you want to study, look out for the icons below which mark different parts of the text.

This icon shows you the activities that you should complete. You write your answers in the spaces provided. You might find it useful to have some spare paper to work on for some of the activities. After you have worked through all the activities on the page, turn to pages 45–49 at the end of this book to check your answers. When you are sure that you understand the topic, put a tick in the box beside it on the Contents page.

On pages 13, 22, 28 and 35 you will find **Progress tests**. These contain questions that will check your understanding of the topics that you have worked through so far. Check your answers on page 50. It is important that you correct any mistakes before moving on to the next section.

On pages 41–44 you will find a **Final test**. This will check your understanding of all the topics. Check your answers on page 51.

Explanation

This text explains the topic and gives examples. Make sure you read it before you start the activities.

This text gives you useful background information about the subject.

Contents

☐	Number stories	4
☐	Choosing operations 1	5
☐	Choosing operations 2	6
☐	Inverses and missing numbers	7
☐	Missing number questions	8
☐	Solving word problems 1	9
☐	Solving word problems 2	10
☐	Solving word problems 3	11
☐	Problems involving place value	12
☐	**Progress test 1**	**13**
☐	Number puzzles	14
☐	Being systematic	15
☐	Correspondence problems	16
☐	Scaling problems	17
☐	Shape puzzles	18
☐	Spotting patterns	19
☐	Recording	20
☐	Square numbers	21
☐	**Progress test 2**	**22**
☐	Money problems 1	23
☐	Money problems 2	24
☐	Measurement problems	25
☐	Time problems 1	26
☐	Time problems 2	27
☐	**Progress test 3**	**28**
☐	Problems with remainders 1	29
☐	Problems with remainders 2	30
☐	Problems involving large numbers	31
☐	Negative number problems	32
☐	Problems involving fractions	33
☐	Problems involving decimals	34
☐	**Progress test 4**	**35**
☐	Ratio problems 1	36
☐	Ratio problems 2	37
☐	Problems involving the distributive law	38
☐	Similar shapes	39
☐	Problems involving percentages	40
☐	**Final test**	**41**
	Answers	**45**

Number stories

Explanation

A number story is a story that can also be written as a number fact.

We can use any real life situation to make a number story for a number fact.

Example
These stories are both for the number fact
3 × **4** = **12**.

- Three dogs each have four legs.
  This makes twelve legs altogether.
- There are four plates on a table.
  Three tomatoes are put on each plate.
  Twelve tomatoes are used.

Did you know?

An ancient Egyptian document, written over 3000 years ago before the addition and subtraction signs were invented, shows addition as a pair of legs walking forwards and subtraction as a pair of legs walking backwards.

I have walked seven steps and
I walk forwards three more steps. **7 + 3**

I have walked seven steps and
I walk backwards three steps. **7 – 3**

Activities

1 Write the number fact for each of these stories.

a I had £**10** and gave £**3** to my sister, leaving me with £**7**. ____________

b My dad shared fifteen sweets equally between three of us.
We each got five sweets. ____________

c Five chairs in my kitchen each have four legs.
This is twenty legs altogether. ____________

2 Make up a number story for each of these facts.

a **9 – 3 = 6** ________________________

____

b **2 × 4 = 8** ________________________

____

c **12 ÷ 2 = 6** ________________________

____

Choosing operations 1

Explanation

Addition, subtraction, multiplication and division are all called **operations**.
An operation is when we do something with numbers.
These are the operation signs:  + − × ÷

Choosing the right operation to answer a question

A number story can also be made into a question.

Example

- Number story: There were six potatoes in a bag. Four got used. Two potatoes were left. **6 − 4 = 2**
- Question: There were six potatoes in a bag. Four got used. How many were left? **6 − 4 = ?**

Activities

1 For each of these number stories choose the correct operation sign to complete the number fact.

a A bus has eight passengers. Three passengers get off the bus. There are now five passengers on the bus. **8 □ 3 = 5**

b A tricycle has three wheels. Six tricycles have eighteen wheels. **3 □ 6 = 18**

c Three ladybirds were on a leaf. One flew away. Now there are two. **3 □ 1 = 2**

d My dad had ten sweets. He shared them out between two people. They each got five sweets. **10 □ 2 = 5**

2 Answer these number story questions.

a A bicycle has two wheels.
How many wheels do five bicycles have? 

b Seven ladybirds were on a leaf.
Two flew away. Now how many are there? 

c My dad had eight sweets. He shared them out
between two people. How many did they each get? 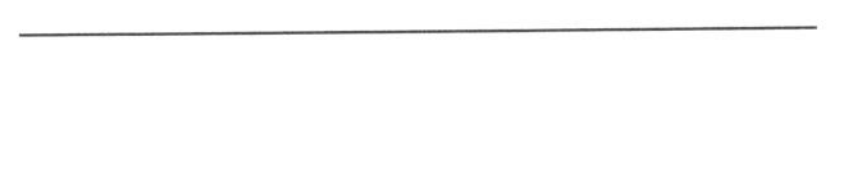

d Nine people were on a bus. Six more got on.
How many are on the bus now? ______

Choosing operations 2

Explanation

Choosing the right operation to complete a number fact

If you are given a number fact without an operation sign, you can use the information below to help you work out which sign is missing.

The following statements are true where **all the numbers** in the number fact are **positive whole numbers.**

- If you add or multiply, the answer will be the largest number in the number fact.

Example $5 + 3 = 8$ $\quad 11 + 9 = 20$ $\quad 201 + 47 = 248$

$3 \times 5 = 15$ $\quad 8 \times 2 = 16$ $\quad 25 \times 5 = 125$

- If you subtract or divide, the first number will be the largest in the number fact.

Example $24 - 4 = 20$ $\quad 50 - 49 = 1$ $\quad 100 - 32 = 68$

$24 \div 6 = 4$ $\quad 50 \div 2 = 25$ $\quad 100 \div 25 = 4$

Activities

1 Fill in the missing operation sign to make these number facts correct.

a 50 ☐ 2 = 25 **b** 50 ☐ 2 = 48 **c** 50 ☐ 2 = 100

d 45 ☐ 15 = 60 **e** 30 ☐ 2 = 32 **f** 64 ☐ 2 = 128

g 55 ☐ 75 = 130 **h** 42 ☐ 6 = 7 **i** 38 ☐ 19 = 19

2 Now make up a number story for facts 'a' to 'c' in activity 1.

a ______________________________

____

b ______________________________

____

c ______________________________

____

Inverses and missing numbers

Explanation

Inverses

The operation that undoes another operation is called its **inverse**.
For example, if you add **5** then you can subtract **5** to 'undo' it.

Subtraction is the inverse of **addition**.	**17 + 5 = 22**	**22 − 5 = 17**
Addition is the inverse of **subtraction**.	**17 − 3 = 14**	**14 + 3 = 17**
Division is the inverse of **multiplication**.	**4 × 3 = 12**	**12 ÷ 3 = 4**
Multiplication is the inverse of **division**.	**20 ÷ 5 = 4**	**4 × 5 = 20**

Activities

1 What is the inverse operation for:

a division? ____________ b subtraction? ____________

c addition? ____________ d multiplication? ____________

Missing numbers

Inverses can be used to solve missing number questions:

37 + □ = 69 In an **addition** fact like this, the **answer** is the **largest number**, The missing number must be **smaller than 69**.

Use the **inverse** operation. **Subtraction** is the inverse of **addition**.

69 − 37 = 32 The missing number is **32**.

□ ÷ 5 = 7 In a **division** fact like this, the **first number** is the **largest**, The missing number must be **larger than 7**.

Use the **inverse** operation. **Multiplication** is the inverse of **division**.

7 × 5 = 35 The missing number is **35**.

2 Work out the missing number in each of these number facts.

a **65 + □ = 96** b **6 × □ = 30** c **□ − 54 = 11**

d **□ ÷ 4 = 8** e **□ + 16 = 30** f **□ × 4 = 28**

Missing number questions

Explanation

Watch out for missing number subtractions and divisions where the missing number is the second number, like these.

55 – ☐ = 31 — In a **subtraction** fact like this, the **first number** is the **largest**, The missing number must be **smaller than 55**.

Here, you do **not** need to use the inverse operation. Adding would make the number larger than **55**. You can just rearrange the subtraction, like this:

55 – 31 = ☐ — The missing number is **24**.

---

36 ÷ ☐ = 4 — In a **division** fact like this, the **first number** is the **largest**, The missing number must be **smaller than 36**.

Here, you do **not** need to use the inverse operation. Multiplying would make the number larger than **36**. You can just rearrange the division, like this:

36 ÷ 4 = ☐ — The missing number is **9**.

Activities

1 Work out the missing number by rearranging the subtraction or division.

a 65 – ☐ = 21 ☐ ☐ ☐ = ☐

b 16 ÷ ☐ = 8 ☐ ☐ ☐ = ☐

c 30 – ☐ = 16 ☐ ☐ ☐ = ☐

d 20 ÷ ☐ = 5 ☐ ☐ ☐ = ☐

e 74 – ☐ = 23 ☐ ☐ ☐ = ☐

f 45 ÷ ☐ = 5 ☐ ☐ ☐ = ☐

2 Work out the missing numbers. For some you will need to use inverses.

a 32 + ☐ = 47 **b** 3 × ☐ = 27 **c** 55 – ☐ = 42

d ☐ ÷ 3 = 6 **e** ☐ + 23 = 30 **f** ☐ × 2 = 14

g ☐ – 35 = 41 **h** 74 – ☐ = 23 **i** 18 ÷ ☐ = 2

Solving word problems 1

Explanation

When looking at word problems, these words can help you to decide what to do.

Addition	**plus**, **and**, **add**, **altogether**, **total**, **increase by**, **more**, **sum**
Subtraction	**take away**, **less**, **difference**, **minus**, **decrease by**, **fewer**, **left**
Multiplication	**product**, **multiply**, **groups of**, **times**, **double**, **twice**, **squared**
Division	**divide**, **share**, **half**, **halve**, **quarter**, **remainder**

Activities

1 Look for useful words and write the **operation** you would use to solve these problems.

	Word problem	Operation
a	James is **42** years old and his daughter is half his age. How old is she?	division
b	Some children get into groups of four. There are eight groups. How many children are there?	
c	My grandma has eight sweets. She shares them between four of us. How many do we each get?	
d	Fifteen people were on a bus. Eleven more got on. Now how many are on the bus?	

2 Which **operation** would you use? Think carefully about these – you may be tricked!

	Word problem	Operation
a	Oliver has **10** fewer stickers than Imogen. Oliver has **25**. How many does Imogen have?	
b	**24** children in a class get into groups of four. How many groups are there?	

Did you know?

Watch out – although these words can often show you what to do, always think carefully about the problem because you can be tricked! Look at this …
I went swimming four times last week and three times this week. How many times did I go swimming?
This is an **addition** question even though the word **times** appears!

Solving word problems 2

Explanation

When faced with a problem, follow these steps:

- read the problem carefully
- look for any useful words in the question
- write down any important numbers in the question
- decide what operations to use
- get an approximate answer
- decide whether to use a written or mental method, and work it out
- finally check your answer.

Example **3363** adults and **4762** children were at a theme park.
How many people were at the theme park?

- Find the important numbers. **3363** **4762**
- Add the two numbers.
- Approximately **3000** + **5000** = about **8000**.
- Work it out.

$$\begin{array}{r} 3363 \\ +\ 4762 \\ \hline 8125 \\ \hline {\scriptstyle 1\,1} \end{array}$$

(written method)

→ Now check whether **8125** people is about right.

Activities

1 Solve these word problems using the steps listed above. Think carefully and use spare paper if you need to.

a There are three times as many cars in a car park on Monday as on Sunday. **48** cars were parked here on Sunday. How many cars are there on Monday? ______

b **9543** people visited the Coliseum cinema this year. This was **2704** more than last year. How many people visited the cinema last year? ______

c Ella's mum is five times older than Ella. Ella is **6**. How old is her mum? ______

d A library has **80** books on each shelf. There are **6** shelves. How many books are there? ______

e A car park has **785** spaces of which **57** are empty. How many cars are in the car park? ______

Solving word problems 3

Explanation

Some problems have **one step** – where there is only one operation, like this one:

Example 41 birds are in a tree. **25** more arrive. How many are in the tree now?

You could solve it like this: **41 + 25 = 66**

Some problems have **two steps**, like this.

Example 41 birds are in a tree. **25** more arrive but **13** leave. How many are in the tree now?

You could solve it like this:

Step one **41 + 25 = 66** Step two **66 – 13 = 53**

Or like this:

Step one **25 – 13 = 12** Step two **41 + 12 = 53**

Activities

1 Solve these one-step word problems.

a **82** cars are in the car park. **15** more arrive. How many cars are there now? __________

b A teacher has **18** grey pencils and **15** coloured pencils. How many pencils does he have in total? __________

c My mum is four times older than me. She is **32**. How old am I? __________

d There are five shelves. A supermarket has **20** tins of beans on each shelf. How many tins are there? __________

2 Solve these two-step word problems.

a **25** cars are in the car park. **8** leave but **17** more arrive. How many cars are there now? __________

b A teacher has **18** grey pencils and **15** coloured pencils. He gives away six pencils. How many pencils does he have in total now? __________

c My mum is three times older than me. She is **30**. How old will I be in **5** years' time? __________

d There are five shelves. A supermarket has **20** tins of beans on each shelf. **32** tins get sold. How many tins are there now? __________

Problems involving place value

Explanation

When solving addition and subtraction problems that include larger numbers, it is helpful to check whether these can be easily solved in your head using place value.

Example George had £**4769** and paid £**1060** for a new TV. He is also given £**1200** for selling his car. How much money has he now?

Th H T U			
4 7 6 9	−	**1 0 6 0**	Reduce the thousands digit by **1** and the tens digit by **6**.
3 7 0 9	+	**1 2 0 0**	Increase the thousands digit by **1** and the hundreds digit by **2**.
£ **4 9 0 9**			

Activities

1 Answer these place value problems mentally.

a There were **4183** men and **3204** women at a football match. How many adults were there altogether? __________

b A male elephant is **3834**mm tall. A female elephant is **702**mm shorter. How tall is she? __________

c Two televisions are for sale. One costs £**304** more than the other. If the cheaper television costs £**474**, what does the more expensive one cost? __________

d Three local schools raise money for charity. St Paul's raises £**212**, Hillside raises £**305** and Chalkwell raises £**270**. How much more than £**500** did they raise in total? __________

2 Some of these problems can be answered mentally and for some you may need to use another method.

a There were **4324** women, **3150** men and **1203** children at a football match. How many people were there altogether? __________

b In **1999** Louise was **38** years old. In which year was she born? __________

c In **2011** Simon was **46** years old. In which year was he born? __________

d Alice has £**4645** in a bank account. She pays in £**278** more. How much less than £**5000** has she now? __________

Progress test 1

1 Write the number fact for each of these stories.

a I had £**15** and gave £**7** to my sister, leaving me with £**8**. ____________________

b Three chairs in my kitchen each have four legs.
This is twelve legs altogether. ____________________

2 Make up a number story for each of these facts.

a $5 \times 4 = 20$ ____

____

b $16 \div 2 = 8$ ____

____

3 Answer these number story questions.

a Nine ladybirds were on a leaf. Three flew away.
How many are there now? ____________________

b Fifteen people were on a bus. Eight more got on.
How many are on the bus now? ____________________

4 Fill in the missing operation signs to make these correct.

a 100 ☐ 2 = 50 **b** 100 ☐ 2 = 98 **c** 100 ☐ 2 = 200

d 25 ☐ 5 = 20 **e** 48 ☐ 2 = 50 **f** 75 ☐ 2 = 150

5 What is the inverse operation for:

a division? ____________________ **b** addition? ____________________

6 Work out the missing numbers. For some you will need to use inverses and for others you will need to rearrange the subtraction or division.

a 32 + ☐ = 47 **b** 3 × ☐ = 27 **c** 58 – ☐ = 42

d ☐ ÷ 3 = 7 **e** ☐ + 16 = 30 **f** ☐ × 2 = 18

7 Solve these problems.

a Abigail scored **4742** points and Hollie scored **2586**.
How many more points did Abigail score than Hollie? ____________________

b In **1999** Zoe was **17** years old. In which year was she born? ____________________

Number puzzles

Did you know?

Carl Friedrich Gauss (1777–1855) was a mathematical genius. It is said that by the time he was three years old he had taught himself how to read and write.

When Gauss was about ten years old his class was set a number puzzle by his primary school teacher. The teacher wanted to keep the pupils busy for a while so asked them to add together all the numbers from **1** to **100**.

Gauss came up with the correct answer in less than a minute. How did he do it?

Explanation

Look at this puzzle.

Find the total of all the numbers from 1 to 9.
(find pairs that make 10)

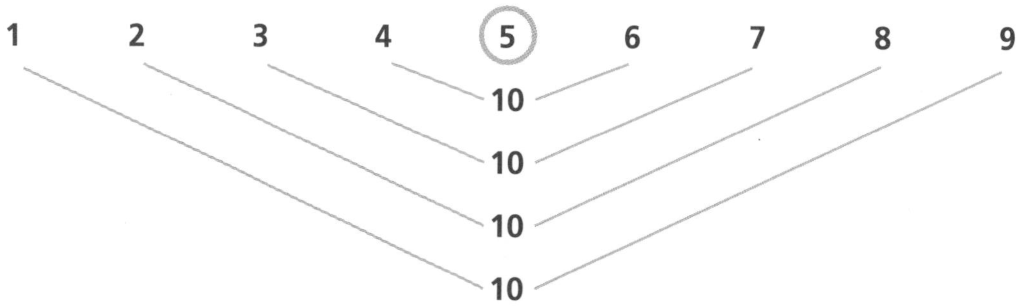

Four pairs that make 10 and the number (5) in the middle makes 40 + 5 = 45.

Activities

1 Find the total of all the numbers from:

a **11** to **19** (find pairs that make 30) ☐

11 12 13 14 (15) 16 17 18 19

30

b **21** to **29** (find pairs that make 50) ☐

21 22 23 24 (25) 26 27 28 29

50

c **1** to **19** (find pairs that make 20) ☐

1 2 3 4 5 6 7 8 9 (10) 11 12 13 14 15 16 17 18 19

20

d **1** to **24** (find pairs that make 25 – there is no middle number this time) ☐

1 2 3 4 5 6 7 8 9 10 11 12 13 14 15 16 17 18 19 20 21 22 23 24

25

2 Can you work out the answer to Gauss's problem using the same method? ☐

Being systematic

Explanation

Be systematic when solving a puzzle. Being systematic means working in a sensible order, like this.

Example Find all the possible pairs of whole numbers with a total of 10.

0 + 10	and	**10 + 0**
1 + 9	and	**9 + 1**
2 + 8	and	**8 + 2**
3 + 7	and	**7 + 3**
4 + 6	and	**6 + 4**
5 + 5		

Notice that the numbers have been written in order.

Activities

1 Find all the possible pairs of whole numbers with a total of **14**.

0 + 14 and 14 + 0

2 Four children, Alec, Ben, Charlie and Dev, stand in a row. Their initials are A, B, C and D. Finish this list to show all the possible orders they could stand in. Notice how they are arranged systematically.

A B C D	B A C D	C A B D	D A __ __
A B D C	B A D C	C A __ __	__ __ __ __
A C B D	B C A D	C B A D	D B __ __
A C D B	B C D A	C B __ __	__ __ __ __
A D B C	B D A C	C D A B	D C __ __
A D C B	B D __ __	__ __ __ __	__ __ __ __

3 Write all six possible orders of writing the letters X, Y, Z. Be systematic.

______ ______ ______ ______ ______ ______

4 Three **odd** numbers are added to make **9**. Find all the different sets of odd numbers with a total of **9**. Be systematic.

1 + 1 + ____

1 + ____ + ____

Correspondence problems

Explanation

Some problems, sometimes known as **correspondence problems**, involve two sets of objects that are linked in some way.

Example
A sandwich shop has three types of sliced bread (white, brown and malted) and four different sandwich fillings (tuna, cheese, chicken and jam). How many different combinations are there for a sandwich made with one type of bread and one filling?

	White	Brown	Malted
Tuna	white with tuna	brown with tuna	malted with tuna
Cheese	white with cheese	brown with cheese	malted with cheese
Chicken	white with chicken	brown with chicken	malted with chicken
Jam	white with jam	brown with jam	malted with jam

A table can help you see the combinations, but notice that for three types of bread and four fillings there are **3** × **4** = **12** combinations altogether.

Activities

1 Complete the table to show how many outfits you can make with three T-shirts and three pairs of trousers.

	Black trousers	Brown trousers	Blue trousers
Red T-shirt	red T-shirt and black trousers		
Blue T-shirt			
White T-shirt			

2 Write how many outfits you can make with four T-shirts and five pairs of trousers. ________________

3 A shop sells two types of T-shirts – ones with stripes and ones with spots. Both types come in four colours. How many different T-shirts do they sell? ________________

4 A florist sells roses, carnations and lilies. Each type of flower comes in pink, white, yellow and red. How many different combinations are there? ________________

5 For school dinners there are three choices of main course and five choices of dessert. How many different two-course meal choices are there? ________________

Scaling problems

Explanation

Example

A sweet shop has a special offer. For every three sweets you buy, they give you two sweets for free. How many free sweets will you get if you buy **24** sweets?

As the number of sweets you buy increases, so does the number you get free. This is known as **scaling**. By writing the multiples of **3** and then the multiples of **2** beneath them you can see a pattern:

Number of sweets you buy:	**3**	**6**	**9**	**12**	**15**	**18**	**21**	**24**
Number of sweets you get free:	**2**	**4**	**6**	**8**	**10**	**12**	**14**	**16** ↑

Each pair of numbers shows you how many you would get free for each number of sweets you buy. So if you buy **24** sweets you get **16** sweets free.

Activities

1 A sweet shop has a special offer. For every five sweets you buy, they give you three sweets for free. Complete the lines of multiples.

Number of sweets you buy:	**5**	**10**	____	____	____	____	____
Number of sweets you get free:	**3**	**6**	____	____	____	____	____

How many free sweets will you get if you buy **35** sweets? ____________

2 Tennis balls are sold in packs of four balls. Each pack costs £**7**. Complete the multiples.

Cost:	£**7**	£ ____	____	____	____	____	____	____	____
Number of balls:	**4**	**8**	____	____	____	____	____	____	____

How many balls would you get if you paid £**63**? ____________

3 Eggs are sold in boxes of six. Each box costs £**2**.
How many eggs would you get if you paid £**14**? ____________

4 A new plant grows eight new leaves every three years.
How many leaves will it have grown after **27** years? ____________

Shape puzzles

Explanation

When exploring shape puzzles, be systematic by working in a sensible order, like this.

Example

This fruit tray has spaces for **four** apples. Sketch all the ways that the tray could look if **none**, **one**, **two**, **three** or **four** apples are in it.

Start with no apples: 

Now one apple: 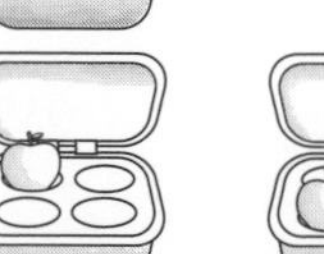 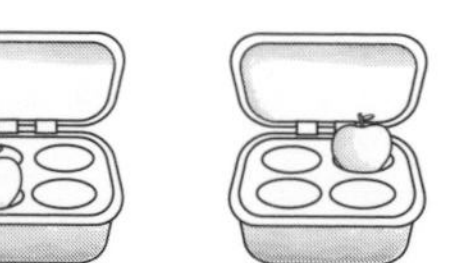 

Now two apples: 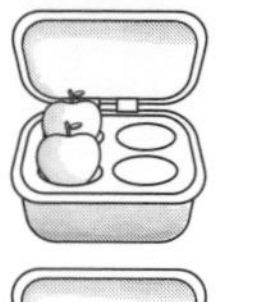  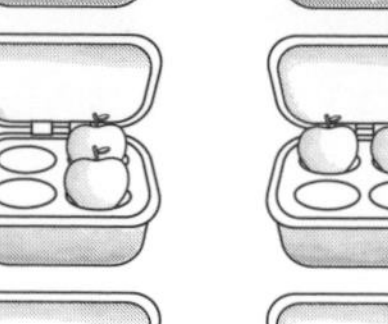  

Now three apples:  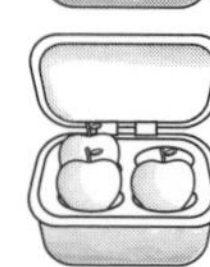 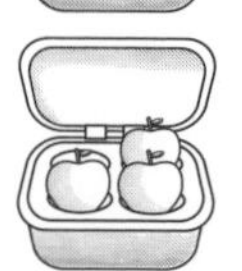 

And finally four:

Total = **16** ways

Activities

1 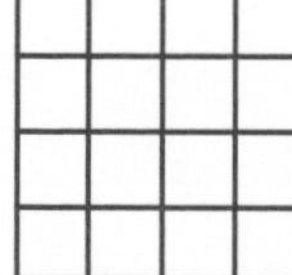

This shape is made from squares of different sizes.

Count the total number of squares in this shape. Be systematic.

Start by counting the small squares

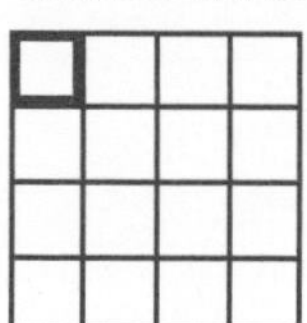

Then the **2 × 2** squares

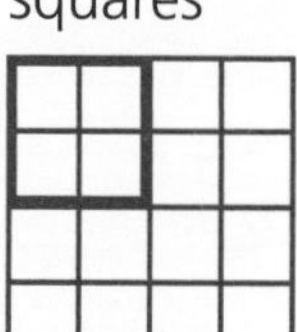

Then the **3 × 3** squares

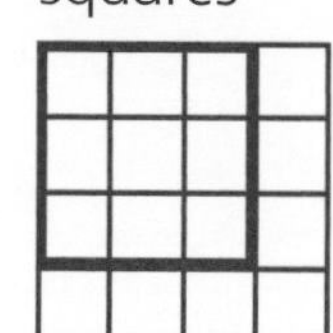

And finally the **4 × 4** square

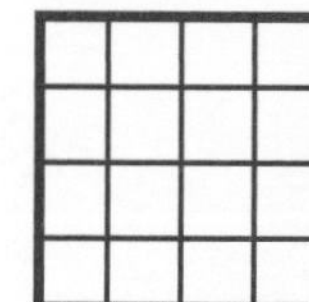

Total = _______ squares

2 

This shape is made from triangles of different sizes.

Count the total number of triangles in this shape. Be systematic.

Total = _______ triangles

Spotting patterns

Explanation

When trying to solve a puzzle or problem, look for patterns.

The shapes in the sequence below are made from small cubes.

1 layer **2 layers** **3 layers** **4 layers**

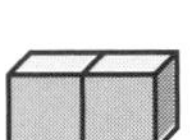

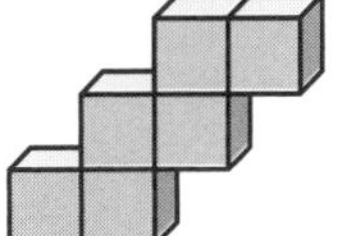

2 cubes **4 cubes** **6 cubes** **8 cubes**

Example How many cubes will a shape with **10 layers** be made from?

Look for patterns in the numbers.

layer 1	=	2 cubes
layer 2	=	4 cubes
layer 3	=	6 cubes
layer 4	=	8 cubes

Do you notice that there are always twice as many cubes as there are layers?

The shape with **10 layers** must have **20 cubes**.

Activities

1 How many cubes will **Shape 10** be made from?

Shape 1 Shape 2  Shape 3  Shape 4 Shape 10

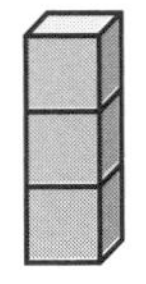

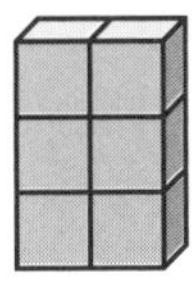

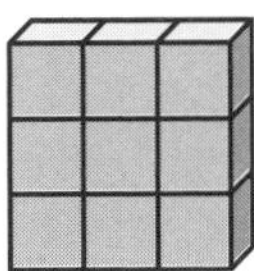

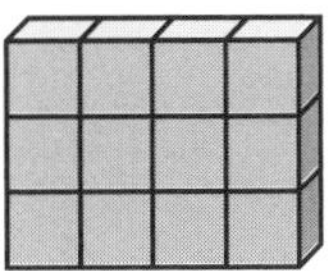

3 cubes 6 cubes _______ cubes _______ cubes _______ cubes

2 How many dots will **Pattern 10** be made from?

Pattern 1 Pattern 2 Pattern 3  Pattern 4 Pattern 10

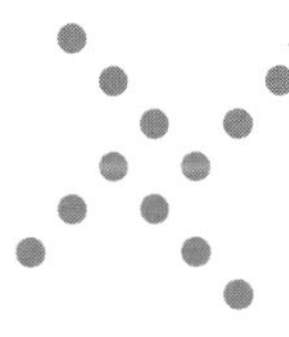

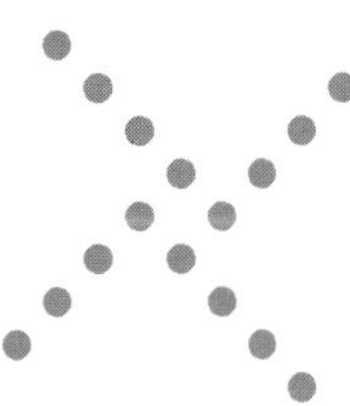

4 dots 8 dots _______ dots _______ dots _______ dots

3 Make up a set of shapes made from dots and work out how many dots will be in the **10**th shape.

Recording

Explanation

Page 15 showed how important it is to be systematic when solving problems. It is also very important to record the results of your work clearly.

Recording your work can help you to see patterns and avoid mistakes.

You can use tables or charts to set your work out clearly. Can you see which type of recording for this puzzle is better?

Example Count the total number of squares in this shape.

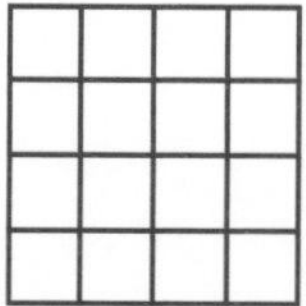

Size of squares	Number
1 × 1	16
2 × 2	9
3 × 3	4
4 × 4	1
Total	**30**

Little squares 16
Bigger squares 9
even bigger 4 Big 1
total = 30

Activities

1 Complete this table to show the results of the problem.
Here is a full set of dominoes. Each domino has a total number of dots. For each total from 0 to 12, work out how many dominoes have this total. For example, only one domino has a total of zero.

Totals	Number
0	1
1	1
2	2
3	
4	
5	
6	
7	
8	
9	
10	
11	
12	

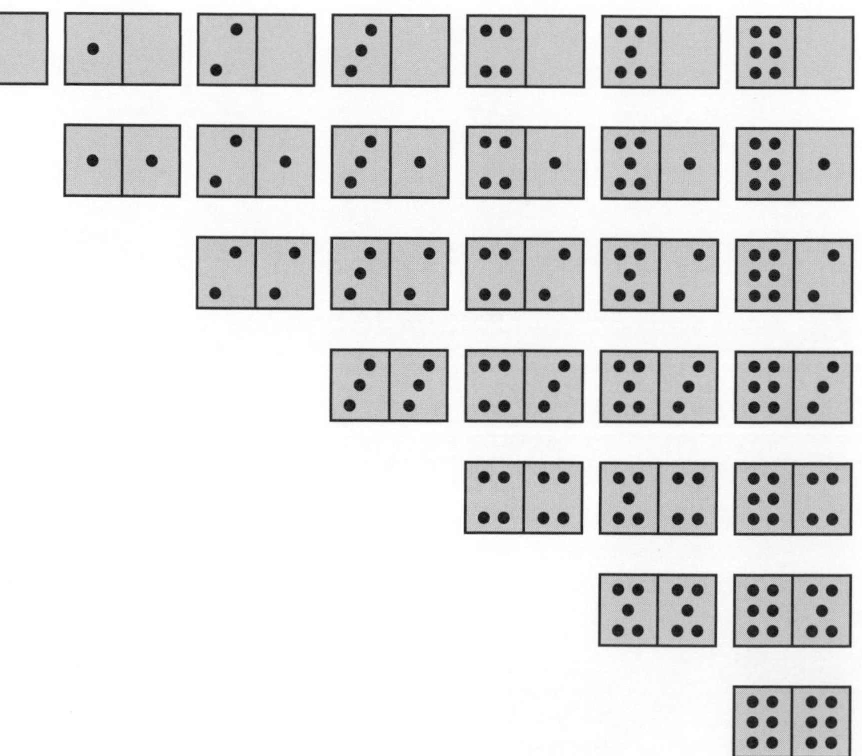

Square numbers

Did you know?

Square numbers are called square because they can be drawn as squares.

They are the result of multiplying a number by itself, like this:

1	4	9	16	25	36
$1 \times 1 = 1$	$2 \times 2 = 4$	$3 \times 3 = 9$	$4 \times 4 = 16$	$5 \times 5 = 25$	$6 \times 6 = 36$

Watch out for square numbers when looking for patterns.

Activities

1 **a** Count the number of cubes in each shape.
Record the results in the table.

Shape 1 Shape 2 Shape 3 Shape 4

Shape	Cubes

b How many cubes will **Shape 10** be made from? ___________

2 **a** Count the number of dots in each pattern.
Record the results in the table.

Pattern 1 Pattern 2 Pattern 3 Pattern 4

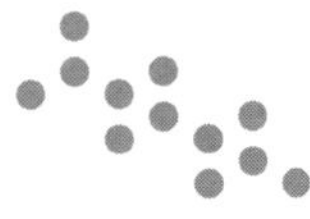

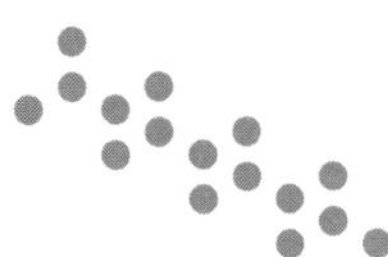

Pattern	Dots

b How many dots will **Pattern 10** be made from? ___________

3 **a** Count the number of stars in each pattern.
Record the results in the table.

Pattern 1 Pattern 2 Pattern 3 Pattern 4

Pattern	Stars

b How many stars will **Pattern 10** be made from? ___________

Progress test 2

1 Find the total of all the numbers from:

a **1** to **9**

1 2 3 4 5 6 7 8 9

b **25** to **35**

25 26 27 28 29 30 31 32 33 34 35

2 Find all the possible pairs of whole numbers with a total of **13**.

3 Be systematic when solving this problem.
This egg box has spaces for six eggs. Shade **all** the ways that the box could look if **one** or **two** eggs are in it.

4 Complete this table to show the results of the problem.

Two dice are rolled and the total is found. What are the possible totals?

Second dice

Totals	1	2	3	4	5	6
1						
2						
3						
4						
5						
6						

First dice

5 a Count the number of cubes in each shape.
Record the results in the table.

Shape 1 Shape 2 Shape 3 Shape 4

Shape	Cubes

b How many cubes will **Shape 10** be made from? ___________

6 Write the first **ten** square numbers.

Money problems 1

Did you know?

Did you know that it is wrong to write amounts of money using both the pounds and the pence signs?

£**5.87**p ✗

If the amount has a decimal point just use the pound sign.

Decimal point
↓
£**5.87**

Activities

1 Write these amounts correctly using a pound sign and a decimal point.

a three pounds and fifty-eight pence ______________

b seven pounds and twenty-two pence ______________

c nine pounds and forty-three pence ______________

d twelve pounds and six pence ______________

2 Solve these one-step money problems.

a I had **58**p and I spent **24**p. How much do I have left? ______________

b Leo was given £**20** for his birthday and £**15** for Christmas. How much did he get in total? ______________

c Jack is paid £**100** every month. How much does he earn in a year (**12** months)? ______________

d Grandma emptied her money box and shared the amount between her three grandchildren. The box had £**12**. How much did each child get? ______________

e A burger costs £**2.20**. Mr Wildman buys four burgers for his children. How much does he pay? ______________

3 Solve these two-step money problems.

a I had **49**p. I was given **20**p more and then I spent **54**p. How much do I have left? ______________

b Six peaches cost **66**p. How much does it cost to buy four peaches? ______________

c Amy saves £**1.50** of her pocket money each week. After **10** weeks she buys a CD costing £**10**. How much money does she have left after that? ______________

d Diya buys a pencil costing **48**p and a rubber costing **24**p. How much less than **80**p is this? ______________

Money problems 2

Explanation

There are 100 pence in every pound.

Multiply by 100 to change pounds to pence.
Divide by 100 to change pence to pounds.

£**4**	=	**400**p
£**3.42**	=	**342**p
£**3.05**	=	**305**p
1200p	=	£**12**

Watch the units

Sometimes in money problems two amounts are given, but one might be given in **pounds** and the other might be given in **pence**.

Make sure you change the numbers so that they are both in pounds, or both in pence, like this:

Example I have a £**20** note and I buy a chew costing **10**p. How much change do I get?

Watch out! The answer is not **20** – **10** = **10**. You must change them both to be in pounds or both to be in pence:

£**20.00** – £**0.10** = £**19.90** or **2000**p – **10**p = **1990**p

Activities

1 How many pence is:

a	£**4.52**	452p	**b**	£**3**	______	**c**	£**3.20**	______	**d**	£**9.05** ______
e	£**2.12**	______	**f**	£**4.96**	______	**g**	£**12**	______	**h**	£**20** ______

2 Write these amounts in pounds:

a	**312**p	£3.12	**b**	**450**p	______	**c**	**183**p	______	**d**	**270**p ______
e	**400**p	______	**f**	**1000**p	______	**g**	**1505**p	______	**h**	**3000**p ______

3 Solve these money problems, changing the amounts to either pounds or pence.

a I have £**35** and I spend **20**p. How much do I have now? ______

b Three items cost **40**p, £**3.25** and £**6**. What is the total cost? ______

c I had £**4.52**. I was given **8**p more and then I spent **50**p.
How much do I have left? ______

d Alice saves **80**p of her pocket money each week.
After **10** weeks she buys a CD costing £**7.50**.
How much money does she have left? ______

e Anna buys a pencil costing **68**p and a rubber costing £**1.05**.
How much change does she get from £**5**? ______

Measurement problems

Explanation

Length, mass and capacity

Word problems sometimes involve measurements, such as:

25cm **10**m **3**km **3**kg **400**g **250**ml **6**l

Remember to give the unit when you give your answer.

Watch the units

Sometimes in measurement problems, like with money problems, two amounts are given in different units.

Make sure you change the numbers so that they are both in the same unit.

Activities

1 Solve these measurement problems.

a I have a piece of string that is **80**cm long.
I cut it into four equal pieces. How long is each piece? __________

b A tin of beans weighs **400**g.
How much do three tins weigh? __________

c I pour **300**ml of water into a cup and drink **60**ml.
How much water is left in the cup? __________

d A runner ran **5**km every day for a week.
How many kilometres did he run in total? __________

e A square field has fencing all the way around its perimeter.
One side of the field is **30**m. How much fencing is there? __________

2 Solve these problems.

a I have a piece of ribbon that is **2**m long. I need pieces of ribbon that are **25**cm long. How many pieces can I cut? __________

b Three items weigh **1**kg, **250**g and **0.5**kg.
What is the total mass of the three items? __________

c A runner ran **500**m every day for **20** days.
How much further than **6**km did he run in total? __________

d There are **2.2**kg of sugar in a bag.
How many grams are there in five bags? __________

Time problems 1

Explanation

Calculating with time

You may be asked to find how long a programme or event goes on for and when it started or finished. **Do not** use a calculator when dealing with time – you'll get the wrong answer!

Example A '1 hour **40** minute' TV programme starts at **9.30** a.m. What time does it end?

Add or subtract the whole hours first and then count on or count back the extra minutes.

9.30 a.m. + **1** hour → **10.30** a.m., then **count on 40** mins → **11.10 a.m.**

Example A '**2** hour **45** minute' tennis match ends at **5.25** p.m. What time did it start?

5.25 p.m. – **2** hours → **3.25** p.m., then **count back 45** mins → **2.40 p.m.**

Example If the time now is **21:27**, what time will it be in **3** hours **20** minutes?

21:27 + **3** hours → **00:27**, then **count on 20** mins → **00:47**

Activities

1 Solve these problems in the same way.

a A '**1** hour **45** minute' TV programme starts at **8.30** p.m. What time does it end? __________

b A '**2** hour **20** minute' TV programme starts at **4.50** p.m. What time does it end? __________

c A '**3** hour **5** minute' tennis match ends at **6.05** p.m. What time did it start? __________

d A '**2** hour **15** minute' tennis match ends at **4.55** p.m. What time did it start? __________

e If the time now is **22:50**, what time will it be in **8** hours **12** minutes? __________

2 Solve these problems.

a A cake went in the oven at **10.25** a.m. and came out at **11.15** a.m. How long was it in the oven? __________

b A man went to work at **8.45** a.m. and finished at **5.15** p.m. How long was he at work? __________

c A girl went to sleep at **20:55** and woke at **07:05** the next morning. How long did she sleep for? __________

Time problems 2

Explanation

Converting between units of time

Time problems can also involve converting between units of time, such as from seconds to minutes, minutes to hours, hours to days, days to weeks and so on.

Learn these relationships to help you convert between them.

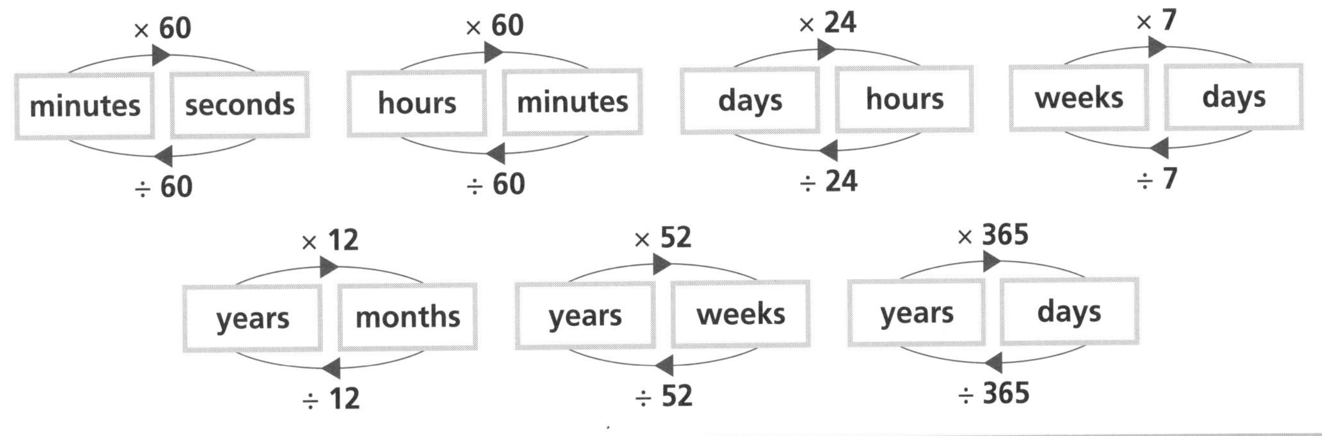

Activities

1 Solve these problems involving converting units of time.

a Sam's plane is due to take off in **53** hours' time. It is now Saturday at **10** a.m. When is Sam's flight? __________

b Luke earns £**200** per month. How much does he earn in three years? __________

c With her mobile phone contract Poppy gets the first four hours of calls free each month. This month she has made **350** minutes of calls. How many minutes will she pay for? __________

d It is nine weeks and five days until Deepa goes on holiday. She decides to save £**1** each day until then to use as spending money. How much spending money will she end up with? __________

e A machine in a factory makes one pencil every second. How many pencils does it make in one hour? __________

f A hard drive can hold **264** hours of TV recording. Theo set his new recorder and left it recording. For how many days would it record before filling the hard drive? __________

Progress test 3

1 Solve these money problems, changing the amounts to pounds or pence.

a Three items cost **70**p, £**3.28** and £**5**.
What is the total cost of the three items? ______________

b Sara buys a coffee costing **78**p and a cake costing £**2.05**.
How much change from £**5** does she get? ______________

c I had £**4.56**. I was given **60**p more and then I spent £**1.35**.
How much do I have left? ______________

2 Solve these measurement problems.

a There are **2.2**kg of flour in a bag.
How many grams are there in two bags? ______________

b I have a piece of string that is **3**m long. I need pieces of string that are **60**cm. How many pieces can I cut? ______________

c Three items weigh **3**kg, **300**g and **0.7**kg.
What is the total mass of the three items? ______________

3 Solve these time problems.

a A boy went to sleep at **21:30** and woke at **07:25** the next morning. How long did he sleep for? ______________

b A '**1** hour **25** minute' TV programme starts at **3.50** p.m.
What time does it end? ______________

c A '**2** hour **20** minute' tennis match ends at **6.05** p.m.
What time did it start? ______________

d Sunil's plane is due to take off in **51** hours' time.
It is now Saturday at **9** a.m. When is Sunil's flight? ______________

e If the time now is **14:55**, what time will it be in **5** hours **50** minutes? ______________

f A man went to work at **8.45** a.m. and finished at **5.30** p.m. How long was he at work? ______________

g A machine in a factory makes one mug every second.
How many mugs does it make in one hour? ______________

Problems with remainders 1

Explanation

When you are faced with a problem that involves division, your answer may include a **remainder**.

How many **4**s in **22**? Answer = **5** remainder **2**

This question can be solved by doing **22** ÷ **4**, and the answer is **5** r **2**.

Remainders don't always make sense. Look at this problem.

Example **22** children are going on a school trip. Each car can carry **four** children. How many cars will be needed?

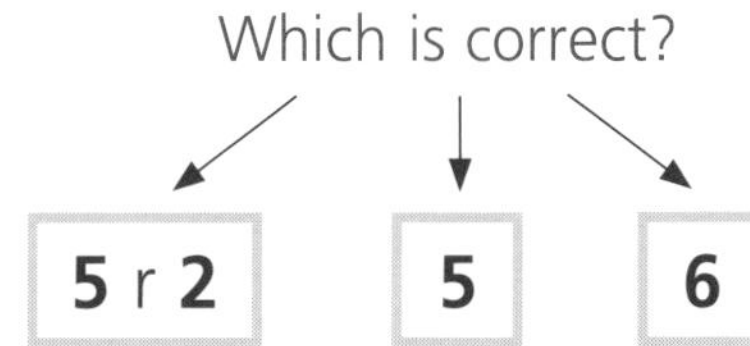

The answer is **6** because, although there will be only two children in the sixth car, that car is still needed.

Watch out for remainders and think carefully about what they mean in each problem. In some problems you will need to round up to the next whole number and in others you will need to round down to the previous whole number.

Activities

1 Solve these problems.

a **46** eggs are put into boxes that each hold six eggs. How many boxes are needed? __________

b **46** eggs are put into boxes that each hold six eggs. How many boxes will be full? __________

c A school has £**62** to buy netballs. Each ball costs £**4**. How many can they buy? __________

d I have **52** cakes. Each box holds eight cakes. How many boxes do I need? __________

e **45** children are going on a school trip. Each car can carry four children. How many cars will be needed? __________

f A florist has **43** roses. She puts them into vases with five roses in each vase. How many full vases are there? __________

g Each page of a photo album holds six photos. What is the smallest number of pages that I need to hold **74** photos? __________

Problems with remainders 2

Explanation

Some division problems are best solved by giving the remainder as a **fraction** or a **decimal**. Look at these two problems.

Example Four people share five cakes equally. How much cake does each person get?

5 ÷ **4** = **1** r **1**

This is not a sensible answer as the remaining cake is also shared between them. The answer $1\frac{1}{4}$ cakes is much more sensible.

Example Four people share £**5** equally. How much does each person get?

5 ÷ **4** = **1** r **1**

This is not a sensible answer as the remaining pound is also shared between them. The answer £**1.25** is much more sensible.

Activities

1 Choose whether you think it is best to give each answer with a remainder, with a fraction, as a decimal or by rounding the answer.

a A **10**m piece of piping is cut into four equal pieces. What is the length of each piece? ________________

b Six pizzas are equally shared between five people. How much pizza did each person have? ________________

c An online photo album shows **12** thumbnail photos on each screen. Jo uploads **50** photos. How many full screens of thumbnail photos will there be? ________________

d **29** children are going to a party by car. If each car can hold up to four children, what is the smallest number of cars needed? ________________

e Three people equally share five bottles of water. How much do they each drink? ________________

f How many **5**p stamps can I buy with **72**p? ________________

g Four people equally share £**30**. How much do they each get? ________________

h I need **66** envelopes. How many packs of four must I buy? ________________

Problems involving large numbers

Explanation

It is important to know the value of digits in large numbers when solving problems. This chart shows the number four million, four hundred and forty-four thousand, four hundred and forty-four, which is written as **4444444**.

Millions	*Hundred thousands*	*Ten thousands*	*Thousands*	*Hundreds*	*Tens*	*Units*
4	**4**	**4**	**4**	**4**	**4**	**4**
↓	↓	↓	↓	↓	↓	↓
4000000	+ **400000**	+ **40000**	+ **4000**	+ **400**	+ **40**	+ **4**

Activities

1 Write the value of the digit **7** in each number.

a **47424** ________________

b **738952** ________________

c **7315668** ________________

d **114723** ________________

e **2371889** ________________

f **2709045** ________________

2 Write these numbers in digits.

a four million, seven hundred and twelve thousand, two hundred and sixteen ________________

b nine million, six hundred and two thousand, eight hundred and four ________________

c one million, eleven thousand and fifty-two ________________

3 Solve these problems.

a About one million, five hundred thousand men live in Wales. There are **55000** more women than men living there. About how many men and women live in Wales? ________________

b A company made profits of £**2463002** last year. This year its profits were £**205745** more than last year. How much were they this year? ________________

Negative number problems

Explanation

Temperatures below freezing (**0**°C) are usually written using negative numbers, such as –**4**°C. To find new temperatures when it gets warmer or cooler we can add or subtract the number of degrees that it has changed by. Use a number line, like the one on this thermometer, to help you.

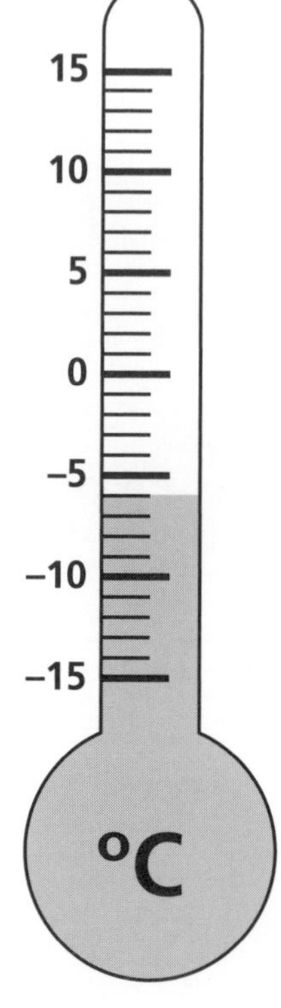

Activities

1 Write the new temperature after each change.

a It was **4**°C. The temperature fell by **7**°C. __________

b It was –**6**°C. The temperature rose by **10**°C. __________

c It was **3**°C. The temperature fell by **10**°C. __________

d It was –**1**°C. The temperature fell by **5**°C. __________

e It was –**9**°C. The temperature rose by **6**°C. __________

2 Solve these problems.

a The temperature in Hasan's fridge is **2**°C. The temperature in his freezer is **18**°C colder than in his fridge. What is the temperature in his freezer? __________

b The temperature in Edinburgh was –**3**°C. The temperature rose by **14**°C by midday. What was the temperature at midday? __________

c In Oslo the temperature is –**17**°C. In Dublin it is **3**°C. How much warmer is it in Dublin than in Oslo? __________

d In December the average temperature is **3**°C warmer than in January. If the average temperature in January is –**4**°C, what is it in December? __________

e On Monday in London the temperature was **14**°C higher than it was in Moscow. By Tuesday the temperature in London had risen **4**°C to **6**°C. What was the temperature in Moscow on Monday? __________

f The temperature in Adam's fridge is **3**°C. The temperature in his freezer is normally **21**°C colder than in the fridge. Adam has left his freezer door slightly open and the temperature in his freezer has risen by **8**°C. What is its current temperature? __________

Problems involving fractions

Explanation

Some problems involve adding, subtracting, multiplying or dividing fractions. Sketch pictures or diagrams to help you work out the answers.

Example

At a restaurant three people eat some pizza.
Each person eats $\frac{3}{4}$ of a pizza.
How much pizza is eaten altogether?

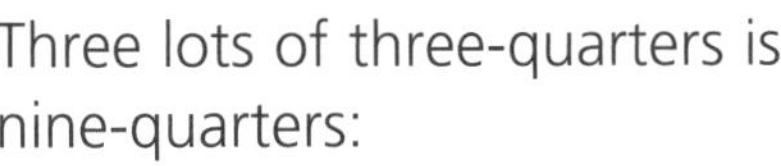

Three lots of three-quarters is nine-quarters:

$3 \times \frac{3}{4} = \frac{9}{4}$

The answer can be written as the improper fraction $\frac{9}{4}$ or as a mixed number $2\frac{1}{4}$.

Activities

1 Solve these problems.

a Jade ate half a pancake. Kate ate a quarter of a pancake.
How much did they eat altogether? __________

b Two children each eat $\frac{5}{6}$ of a cheesecake.
How much cheesecake is eaten? __________

c Three-quarters of a cheesecake is left.
Alex then ate one-eighth of the whole cheesecake.
How much is now left? __________

d Hayleigh had three boxes of chocolates for Christmas.
She ate one-quarter of a box each day for seven days.
How many boxes has she eaten? How many are left? ______ ______

e Kamil, Lara and Daniel were eating curry.
They all ate two-thirds of a poppadom each.
How many poppadoms did they eat altogether? __________

f Elise eats half a pizza and Avani eats one-third.
What fraction of the pizza have they eaten in total? __________

g Some children were asked to vote for their favourite hobby. Two-thirds of them voted for swimming. One-quarter voted for football. The rest voted for video games. What fraction of them voted for video games? __________

Problems involving decimals

Explanation

The digits to the right of the decimal point in a number represent part numbers – tenths, hundredths, thousandths and so on.

units	.	tenths	hundredths	thousandths
6	.	**4**	**8**	**7**

When solving word problems involving adding and subtracting decimals, work in the same way as for whole numbers.

Example What is the total mass of a parcel weighing **0.462**kg and one weighing **0.57**kg?

$$\begin{array}{r} 0.462 \\ +\ 0.57 \\ \hline 1.032 \\ \hline {\scriptstyle 1\ 1\ \ } \end{array}$$

Line up the digits correctly and add (or subtract) in the usual way.

= **1.032**kg

When subtracting, you can write zeros at the end of the first number if it has fewer digits after the decimal point than the number being subtracted.

0.5 – 0.254 = 0.500 – 0.254

Activities

1 Solve these decimal problems.

a Paige has a piece of ribbon that is **5.6**m long. She cuts off a length that is **3.65**m long. How much ribbon is left? ____________________

b What is the total length of a line that is **0.08**cm longer than **5.7**cm? ____________________

c Ruby cycled **23.6**km in the morning and **6.24**km in the afternoon. How far did she cycle altogether? ____________________

d A tin holds **1.2** litres of paint. Ahmed pours out **0.75** litres of it. How much is still in the tin? ____________________

e Josh is **1.65**m tall. His sister is **0.7**m shorter than him. How tall is his sister? ____________________

f A jug holds **0.85** litres of water. Jamie pours out **0.275** litres of it. How much is still in the jug? ____________________

g How much heavier is a box weighing **1.5**kg than one that weighs **1.289**kg? ____________________

Progress test 4

1 Choose whether you think it is best to give each answer with a remainder, with a fraction, as a decimal or by rounding the answer.

a A **6**m piece of string is cut into four equal pieces. What is the length of each piece? __________

b Six pizzas are equally shared between four people. How much pizza did each person have? __________

c £**6** is equally shared between four people. How much does each person get? __________

d A photo album fits four photos on each page. Ola has six photos. How many full pages of photos will there be? __________

2 A company made profits of £**4 843 542** last year. This year its profits were £**803 110** less than last year. How much were they this year? __________

3 Solve these fraction problems.

a Three children each eat $\frac{5}{6}$ of a pie. How many pies are eaten? __________

b Libby had three boxes of chocolates for Christmas. She ate one-third of a box each day for seven days. How many boxes has she eaten? How many are left? ______ ______

4 Solve these decimal problems.

a A tin holds **1.5** litres of paint. Jack pours out **0.7** litres of it. How much is still in the tin? __________

b Sally is **1.15**m tall. Her brother is **0.7**m taller than her. How tall is her brother? __________

c Prisha's new baby boy weighed **3.208**kg at birth. He now weighs **4.5**kg. By how much has his weight increased? __________

Ratio problems 1

Explanation

On page 17 you learnt that you can write multiples of two numbers to work out integer scaling problems. You can use these ideas for solving ratio problems.

Example In a class the ratio of boys to girls is **3:5**. If there are **32** children in the class, how many are boys and how many are girls?

The ratio means that there are three boys for every five girls in the class. We can list multiples of **3** and **5** to help us find where the total is **32** children.

Number of boys:	**3**	**6**	**9**	**12**	**15**	**18**	**...**
Number of girls:	**5**	**10**	**15**	**20**	**25**	**30**	**...**

When there are **12** boys and **20** girls the total is **32**.

Activities

1 At a party the ratio of boys to girls is **2:3**. Complete the lines of multiples.

Number of boys:	2	4	____	____	____	____	____	____	____	____
Number of girls:	3	6	____	____	____	____	____	____	____	____

How many boys and girls are there if there are **40** children at the party?

____________ boys and ____________ girls

2 The ratio of cows to sheep in a field is **5:4**. How many cows and sheep are there if there are **54** animals in the field?

____________ cows and ____________ sheep

3 The ratio of ducks to ducklings on a pond is **1:5**. How many ducks and ducklings are there if there are **30** altogether on the pond?

____________ ducks and ____________ ducklings

4 The ratio of cats to dogs at the vets is **3:4**. How many cats and dogs are there if there are **28** altogether?

____________ cats and ____________ dogs

Ratio problems 2

Explanation

Amounts of money can be split equally such as sharing between four people, and unequally such as sharing money in the ratio **2:5**. This means that the money is split into **7** parts, and that **2** parts are given to one person and **5** parts are given to the other person. When solving problems like these always make sure you know the total number of parts being given out.

Example £**63** is shared between two people in the ratio **4:5**. How much does each person get?

There are **4** + **5** = **9** parts altogether. £**63** divided by **9** = £**7**, so each part is £**7**.

Now multiply to find how much each person will get: **4** × £**7** = £**28** and **5** × £**7** = £**35**.

Always add to make sure they come to the correct total: £**28** + £**35** = £**63**.

Activities

1 Solve these ratio problems.

a £**45** is shared between two people in the ratio **2:3**.
How much does each person get? ____________ and ____________

b £**42** is shared between two people in the ratio **4:3**.
How much does each person get? ____________ and ____________

c £**120** is shared between two people in the ratio **5:7**.
How much does each person get? ____________ and ____________

d £**64** is shared between two people in the ratio **5:3**.
How much does each person get? ____________ and ____________

e £**77** is shared between two people in the ratio **5:6**.
How much does each person get? ____________ and ____________

f £**75** is shared between two people in the ratio **8:7**.
How much does each person get? ____________ and ____________

g £**39** is shared between two people in the ratio **6:7**.
How much does each person get? ____________ and ____________

Problems involving the distributive law

Explanation

When solving multiplication problems it can help to split a number into parts and multiply each part separately.

Example A farmer has six rows of cabbages with **13** cabbages in each row.
How many cabbages altogether?

These diagrams show that the cabbages can be split in different ways and each part multiplied separately. When the parts are added the answers will be the same.

13 split into **4** and **9**

6 × 4 **6 × 9**

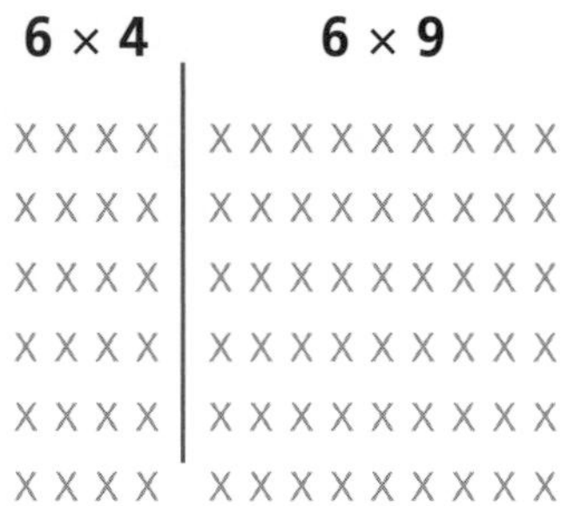

24 **54**

24 + 54 = 78

13 split into **8** and **5**

6 × 8 **6 × 5**

48 **30**

48 + 30 = 78

13 split into **10** and **3**

6 × 10 **6 × 3**

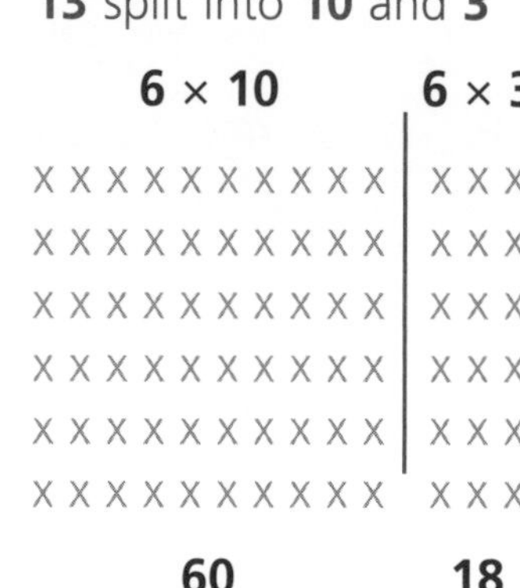

60 **18**

60 + 18 = 78

Split the larger number however you like to make the multiplication easier.

Activities

1 A gardener has four rows of leeks with **17** in each row.
How many leeks altogether? ______

2 A gardener has seven rows of cauliflowers with **19** in each row.
How many cauliflowers altogether? ______

3 Find the area of each of these rectangles.

a **7**cm, **16**cm ______

b

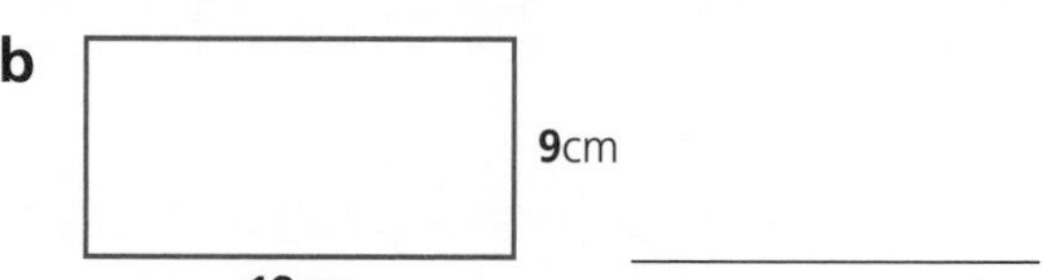

9cm, **18**cm ______

c **14**cm, **6**cm ______

d

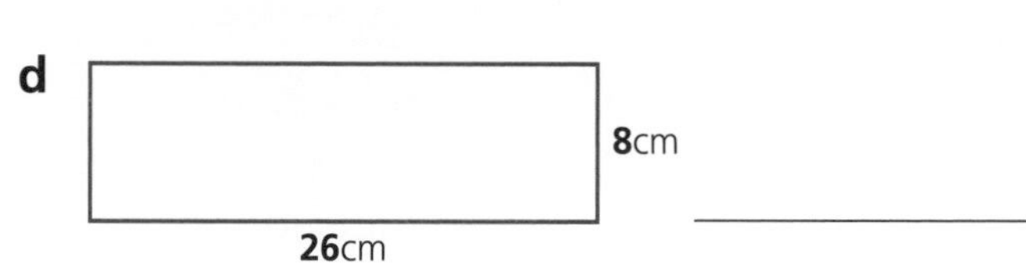

8cm, **26**cm ______

e **4**cm, **37**cm ______

Similar shapes

Explanation

Similar shapes are those which look the same with the same angles but which have been enlarged or reduced in size.

If one side has been enlarged by a particular scale factor, then all sides will have been enlarged in the same way.

These triangles are similar. Each side of the smaller triangle has been multiplied by **1.5** to give the lengths of sides of the larger triangle. This number, **1.5** is known as the **scale factor**. We can find it by dividing one side of the larger shape by the corresponding side of the smaller shape: **4.5** ÷ **3** = **1.5**.

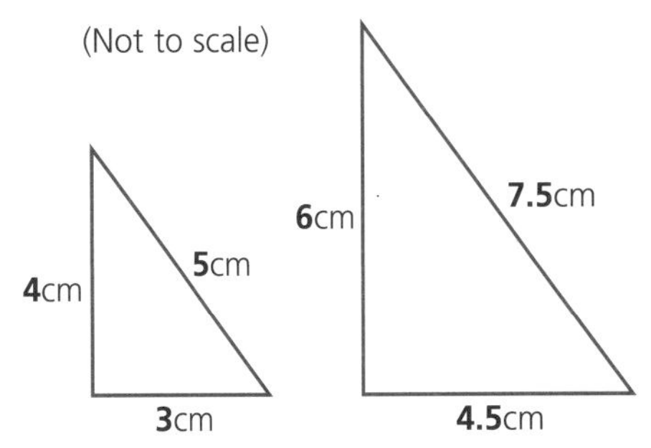

Activities

1 Find the scale factor showing how the smaller shape has been enlarged.

3cm
8cm

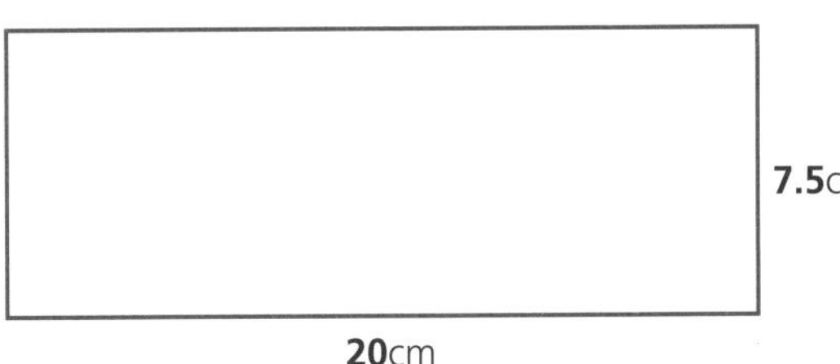

scale factor ______

2 Find the scale factor and use it to help you find the missing lengths.

a

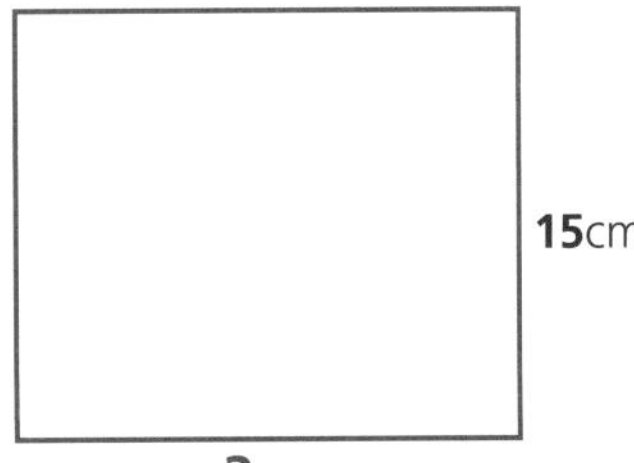

scale factor ______ ______ cm

b

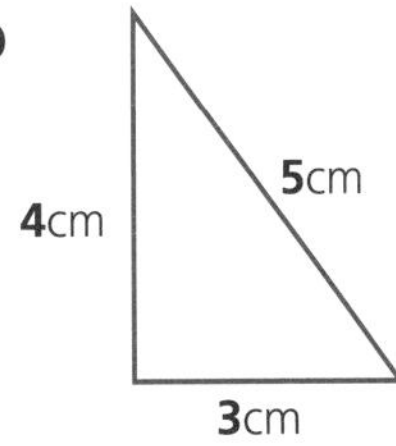

4.8cm
?cm
3.6cm

scale factor ______ ______ cm

c

3.6cm
2.4cm

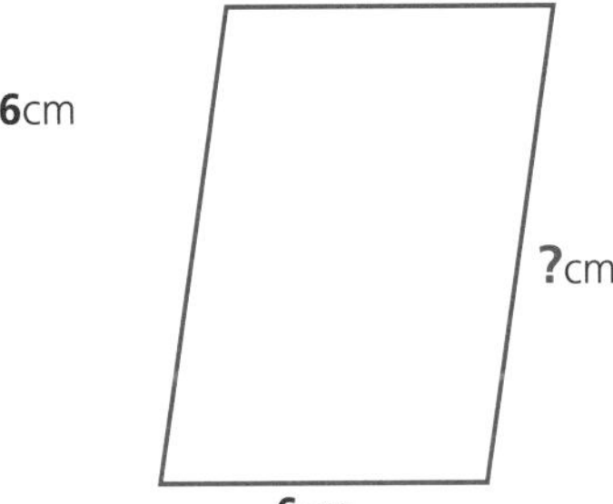

scale factor ______ ______ cm

d

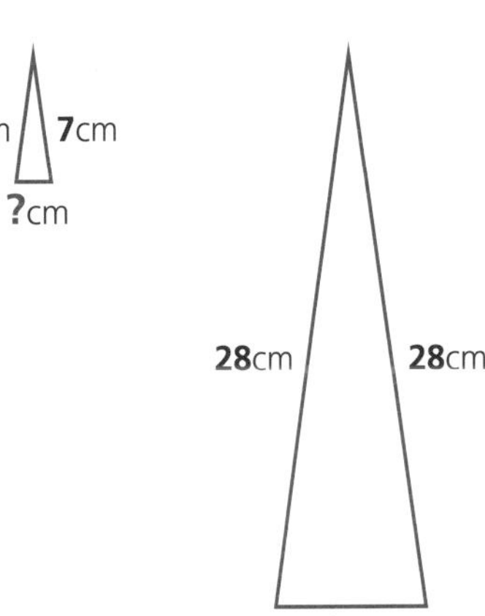

scale factor ______ ______ cm

Problems involving percentages

Explanation

Percentages are parts out of **100**, such as **40**% which means **40** out of **100**. To solve percentage problems, first find easy percentages and use them to find others.

Example

Find **50**% by dividing by **2**, then **25**% by halving the answer.

Find **10**% by dividing by **10**, then **20**% by doubling the answer or **5**% by halving it.

Find **1**% by dividing by **100** and **7**% by multiplying the answer by **7**.

Activities

1 Find the percentages in each row.

a	**10**% of **60** = ____	**20**% of **60** = ____	**40**% of **60** = ____
b	**50**% of **24** = ____	**25**% of **24** = ____	**75**% of **24** = ____
c	**10**% of **320** = ____	**5**% of **320** = ____	**15**% of **320** = ____
d	**1**% of **500** = ____	**2**% of **500** = ____	**8**% of **500** = ____
e	**20**% of **300** = ____	**1**% of **300** = ____	**21**% of **300** = ____
f	**10**% of **80** = ____	**5**% of **80** = ____	**95**% of **80** = ____

2 Solve these decimal problems.

a A school party of **80** children go the London Eye. **30**% of them are girls. How many are girls? ____

b **15**% of the children in Year 6 own a cat. If there are **60** children in Year 6, how many own a cat? ____

c How much greater is **75**% of **48** than **80**% of **40**? ____

d **95**% of sheep on a farm are Suffolks. If there are **600** sheep, how many are **not** Suffolks? ____

e A nurse gives **70**% of a full dose of medicine to a child. If the full dose is **30**ml, how much is the child given? ____

f Of the **2500** people at a football match, **40**% are women, **35**% men and the rest are children. How many are children? ____

Final test

1 Write the number fact for each of these stories.

a I had £**23** and gave £**8** to my sister, leaving me with £**15**. ____________

b Five sheep each have four legs. This is twenty legs altogether. ____________

2 Answer these number story questions.

a **24** cows were in a field. Six more joined them.
How many are there now? ____________

b **32** people were on a bus. Five more got on.
How many are on the bus now? ____________

3 Fill in the missing operation sign to make these correct.

a **40** ☐ **2 = 80** b **40** ☐ **2 = 38** c **40** ☐ **2 = 42**

4 Work out the missing numbers. For some you will need to use inverses and for others you will need to rearrange the subtraction or division.

a **27 +** ☐ **= 52** b **4 ×** ☐ **= 36** c **66 –** ☐ **= 53**

d ☐ **÷ 4 = 8** e ☐ **+ 43 = 50** f ☐ **× 4 = 32**

5 Find the total number of all the numbers from **2** to **18**.

2 3 4 5 6 7 8 9 10 11 12 13 14 15 16 17 18

6 Write all the possible pairs of whole numbers with a total of **15**.

7 Solve these problems.

a There were **4414** men, **2524** women and **3030** children at a football match.
How many people were there altogether? ____________

b In **1999** Robert was **47** years old.
In which year was he born? ____________

c In **2011** Clare was **39** years old.
In which year was she born? ____________

8 Write the first **nine** square numbers.

☐ ☐ ☐ ☐ ☐ ☐ ☐ ☐ ☐

9 Be systematic when solving this problem:
This fruit box has spaces for four peaches. Shade **all** the ways that the box could look if **none, one, two, three or four** peaches are in it.

10 **a** Count the number of cubes in each shape.
Record the results in the table

Shape 1 **Shape 2** **Shape 3** **Shape 4**

Shape	Cubes

b How many cubes will **Shape 10** be made from? ________

11 Solve these one-step word problems.

a **66** cars are in the car park. **37** more arrive.
How many cars are there now? ________

b My mum is four times older than me. I am 7.
How old is my mum? ________

12 Solve these two-step money problems.

a I had **58**p. I was given **30**p more and then I spent **37**p. How much do I have left? ________

b Six apples cost **72**p. How much does it cost to buy five apples? ________

13 Write these amounts correctly using a pound sign and a decimal point.

a five pounds and sixty-eight pence ________

b twelve pounds and four pence ________

14 Solve these money problems, changing the amounts to pounds or pence.

a Three items cost **50**p, £**3.35** and £**8**.
What is the total cost of the three items? ______________

b I had £**4.52**. I was given **9**p more and then
I spent £**1.25**. How much do I have left? ______________

c Pari buys a coffee costing **85**p and a cake costing
£**1.09**. How much change from £**5** does she get? ______________

15 Solve these measurement problems.

a I have a piece of string that is **2**m long.
I need pieces of string that are each **40**cm long.
How many pieces can I cut? ______________

b Three items weigh **2**kg, **200**g and **0.8**kg.
What is the total mass of the three items? ______________

c There are **2.2**kg of sugar in a bag.
How many grams are there in **10** bags? ______________

16 Solve these time problems.

a A '**1** hour **25** minute' TV programme starts at
4.50 p.m. What time does it end? ______________

b A '**2** hour **10** minute' tennis match ends at
5.05 p.m. What time did it start? ______________

c If the time now is **13:35**, what time will it be
in **5** hours **50** minutes? ______________

17 Solve these problems, thinking carefully about remainders.

a A school has £**47** to buy netballs. Each ball costs £**4**.
How many can they buy? ______________

b I have **73** cakes. Each box holds eight cakes.
How many boxes do I need? ______________

c A florist has **63** daffodils. She puts them into vases
with five daffodils in each vase. How many full vases
are there? ______________

18 Solve these problems.

a Eve's plane is due to take off in **63** hours' time.
It is now Monday at **8** a.m. When is Eve's flight? ________________

b With her phone contract Grace gets the first **3** hours of calls free each month. This month she has made **330** minutes of calls. How many minutes will she pay for? ________________

c On Saturday in Paris the temperature was **14**°C higher than it was in Helsinki. By Tuesday the temperature in Paris had risen **2**°C to **3**°C. What was the temperature in Helsinki on Saturday? ________________

d Three-quarters of a cheesecake is left. Then Rasool ate one-sixth of the whole cheesecake. How much is now left? ________________

e The ratio of horses to sheep in a field is **2:7**. How many horses and sheep are there if there are **63** animals in the field?

__________ horses and __________ sheep

f £**42** is shared between two people in the ratio **5:2**. How much does each person get?

__________ and __________

19 Look at these similar rectangles.

6cm
17cm
9cm
?cm

a Find the area of the first rectangle. ________________

b Find the scale factor and use it to help you find the missing length. ________ ________

20 Solve these problems.

a A school party of **96** children go to the Tower of London.
75% of them are girls. How many are girls? ________________

b How much greater is **55**% of £**110** than **80**% of £**70**? ________________

Answers to Activities

Page 4: Number stories

1 **a** 10 – 3 = 7
b 15 ÷ 3 = 5
c 5 × 4 = 20

2 appropriate number stories

Page 5: Choosing operations 1

1 **a** –
b ×
c –
d ÷

2 **a** 10
b 5
c 4
d 15

Page 6: Choosing operations 2

1 **a** ÷ **b** – **c** ×
d + **e** + **f** ×
g + **h** ÷ **i** –

2 appropriate number stories

Page 7: Inverses and missing numbers

1 **a** multiplication **b** addition
c subtraction **d** division

2 **a** 31 **b** 5 **c** 65
d 32 **e** 14 **f** 7

Page 8: Missing number questions

1 **a** 44, 65 – 21 = 44
b 2, 16 ÷ 8 = 2
c 14, 30 – 16 = 14
d 4, 20 ÷ 5 = 4
e 51, 74 – 23 = 51
f 9, 45 ÷ 5 = 9

2 **a** 15 **b** 9 **c** 13
d 18 **e** 7 **f** 7
g 76 **h** 51 **i** 9

Page 9: Solving word problems 1

1 **a** division
b multiplication
c division
d addition

2 **a** addition
b division

Page 10: Solving word problems 2

1 **a** 144
b 6839
c 30
d 480
e 728

Page 11: Solving word problems 3

1 **a** 97
b 33
c 8
d 100

2 **a** 34
b 27
c 15
d 68

Page 12: Problems involving place value

1 **a** 7387
b 3132mm
c £778
d £287

2 **a** 8677
b 1961
c 1965
d £77

Page 14: Number puzzles

1 **a** 135 **b** 225 **c** 190 **d** 300

2 50 × 101 = 5050

Page 15: Being systematic

1

0 + 14	14 + 0
1 + 13	13 + 1
2 + 12	12 + 2
3 + 11	11 + 3
4 + 10	10 + 4
5 + 9	9 + 5
6 + 8	8 + 6
7 + 7	

2

B A C D B A D C	C A B D C A D B	D A B C D A C B
B C A D B C D A	C B A D C B D A	D B A C D B C A
B D A C B D C A	C D A B C D B A	D C A B D C B A

3 XYZ XZY YXZ YZX ZXY ZYX

4

1 + 1 + 7	1 + 7 + 1	7 + 1 + 1
1 + 3 + 5	1 + 5 + 3	
3 + 1 + 5	3 + 5 + 1	
5 + 1 + 3	5 + 3 + 1	
3 + 3 + 3		

Page 16: Correspondence problems

1

red T-shirt and black trousers	red T-shirt and brown trousers	red T-shirt and blue trousers
blue T-shirt and black trousers	blue T-shirt and brown trousers	blue T-shirt and blue trousers
white T-shirt and black trousers	white T-shirt and brown trousers	white T-shirt and blue trousers

2 20

3 8

4 12

5 15

Page 17: Scaling problems

1

5	10	15	20	25	30	35
3	6	9	12	15	18	21

21 free sweets

2

£7	£14	£21	£28	£35	£42	£49	£56	£63
4	8	12	16	20	24	28	32	36

36 balls

3 42

4 72

Page 18: Shape puzzles

1 16 + 9 + 4 + 1 = 30

2 9 + 3 + 1 = 13

Page 19: Spotting patterns

1 30

2 40

3 Answers will depend on the design.

Page 20: Recording

1

Totals	Number
0	1
1	1
2	2
3	2
4	3
5	3
6	4
7	3
8	3
9	2
10	2
11	1
12	1

Page 21: Square numbers

1 a

Shape	Cubes
1	1
2	4
3	9
4	16

b 100

2 a

Pattern	Dots
1	4
2	8
3	12
4	16

b 40

3 a

Pattern	Stars
1	1
2	4
3	9
4	16

b 100

Page 23: Money problems 1

1 **a** £3.58
b £7.22
c £9.43
d £12.06

2 **a** 34p
b £35
c £1200
d £4
e £8.80

3 **a** 15p
b 44p
c £5
d 8p

Page 24: Money problems 2

1 **a** 452p **b** 300p **c** 320p **d** 905p
e 212p **f** 496p **g** 1200p **h** 2000p

2 **a** £3.12 **b** £4.50 **c** £1.83 **d** £2.70
e £4 **f** £10 **g** £15.05 **h** £30

3 **a** £34.80 or 3480p
b £9.65 or 965p
c £4.10 or 410p
d £0.50 or 50p
e £3.27 or 327p

Page 25: Measurement problems

1 **a** 20cm
b 1.2kg or 1200g
c 240ml
d 35km
e 120m

2 **a** 8
b 1.75kg or 1750g
c 4km
d 11 000g

Page 26: Time problems 1

1 **a** 10.15 p.m.
b 7.10 p.m.
c 3.00 p.m.
d 2.40 p.m.
e 07:02

2 **a** 50 minutes
b 8 hours 30 minutes
c 10 hours 10 minutes

Page 27: Time problems 2

1 **a** Monday at 3 p.m.
b £7200
c 110 minutes
d £68
e 3600
f 11 days

Answers to Activities continued

Page 29: Problems with remainders 1

1 **a** 8
b 7
c 15
d 7
e 12
f 8
g 13

Page 30: Problems with remainders 2

1 **a** 2.5m
b $1\frac{1}{5}$
c 4
d 8
e $1\frac{2}{3}$
f 14
g £7.50
h 17

Page 31: Problems involving large numbers

1 **a** 7000 or 7 thousand
b 700 000 or 7 hundred thousand
c 7 000 000 or 7 million
d 700 or 7 hundred
e 70 000 or 70 thousand
f 700 000 or 7 hundred thousand

2 **a** 4 712 216
b 9 602 804
c 1 011 052

3 **a** 3 055 000
b £2 668 747

Page 32: Negative number problems

1 **a** –3°C
b 4°C
c –7°C
d –6°C
e –3°C

2 **a** –16°C
b 11°C
c 20°C
d –1°C
e –12°C
f –10°C

Page 33: Problems involving fractions

1 **a** $\frac{3}{4}$
b $\frac{5}{3}$ or $1\frac{2}{3}$
c $\frac{5}{8}$
d $1\frac{3}{4}$, $1\frac{1}{4}$
e 2
f $\frac{5}{6}$
g $\frac{1}{12}$

Page 34: Problems involving decimals

1 **a** 1.95m
b 5.78cm
c 29.84km
d 0.45 litres
e 0.95m
f 0.575 litres
g 0.211kg or 211g

Page 36: Ratio problems 1

1 2 4 6 8 10 12 14 16 18 20
3 6 9 12 15 18 21 24 27 30
16 boys and 24 girls

2 30 cows and 24 sheep

3 5 ducks and 25 ducklings

4 12 cats and 16 dogs

Page 37: Ratio problems 2

1 **a** £18 and £27
b £24 and £18
c £50 and £70
d £40 and £24
e £35 and £42
f £40 and £35
g £18 and £21

Page 38: Problems involving the distributive law

1 68

2 133

3 **a** $112cm^2$ **b** $162cm^2$
c $84cm^2$ **d** $208cm^2$
e $148cm^2$

Page 39: Similar shapes

1 2.5

2 **a** scale factor 3, 18cm
b scale factor 1.2, 6cm
c scale factor 2.5, 9cm
d scale factor 4, 2cm

Page 40: Problems involving percentages

1 **a** 6, 12, 24
b 12, 6, 18
c 32, 16, 48
d 5, 10, 40
e 60, 3, 63
f 8, 4, 76

2 **a** 24
b 9
c 4
d 30
e 21ml
f 625

Answers to Progress tests

PROGRESS TEST 1 – Page 13

1 **a** 15 – 7 = 8
b 3 × 4 = 12

2 appropriate number stories

3 **a** 6
b 23

4 **a** ÷ **b** – **c** ×
d – **e** + **f** ×

5 **a** multiplication **b** subtraction

6 **a** 15 **b** 9 **c** 16
d 21 **e** 14 **f** 9

7 **a** 2156
b 1982

PROGRESS TEST 2 – Page 22

1 **a** 45 **b** 330

2

0 + 13	13 + 0
1 + 12	12 + 1
2 + 11	11 + 2
3 + 10	10 + 3
4 + 9	9 + 4
5 + 8	8 + 5
6 + 7	7 + 6

3

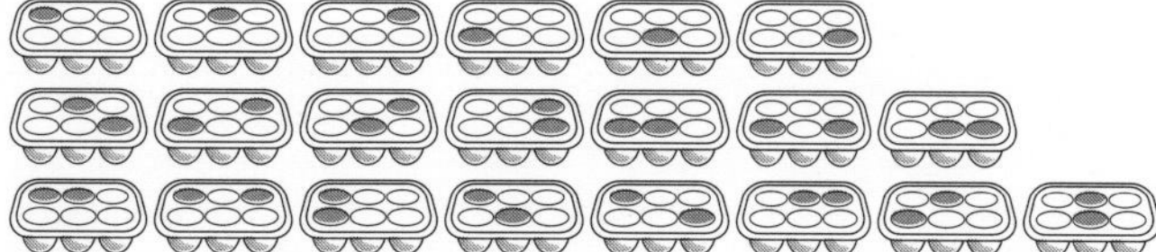

4

2	3	4	5	6	7
3	4	5	6	7	8
4	5	6	7	8	9
5	6	7	8	9	10
6	7	8	9	10	11
7	8	9	10	11	12

5 **a**

Shape	Cubes
1	5
2	10
3	15
4	20

b 50

6 1, 4, 9, 16, 25, 36, 49, 64, 81, 100

PROGRESS TEST 3 – Page 28

1 **a** £8.98
b £2.17
c £3.81

2 **a** 4400g
b 5
c 4kg

3 **a** 9 hours 55 minutes
b 5.15 p.m.
c 3.45 p.m.
d Monday at 12.00 noon
e 20:45
f 8 hours 45 minutes
g 3600

PROGRESS TEST 4 – Page 35

1 **a** 1.5m
b $1\frac{1}{2}$
c £1.50
d 1

2 £4 040 432

3 **a** $2\frac{1}{2}$
b $2\frac{1}{3}, \frac{2}{3}$

4 **a** 0.8 litres
b 1.85m
c 1.292kg or 1292g

Answers to Final test

FINAL TEST – Pages 41–44

1 **a** 23 – 8 = 15
b 5 × 4 = 20

2 **a** 30
b 37

3 **a** × **b** – **c** +

4 **a** 25 **b** 9 **c** 13
d 32 **e** 7 **f** 8

5 170

6

0 + 15	15 + 0
1 + 14	14 + 1
2 + 13	13 + 2
3 + 12	12 + 3
4 + 11	11 + 4
5 + 10	10 + 5
6 + 9	9 + 6
7 + 8	8 + 7

7 **a** 9968
b 1952
c 1972

8 1, 4, 9, 16, 25, 36, 49, 64, 81, 100

9

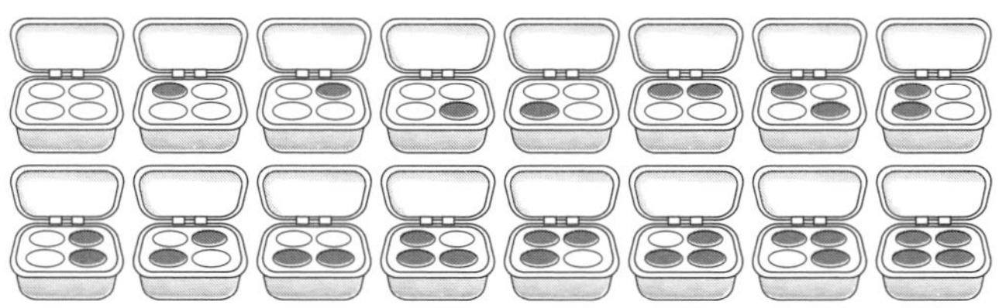

10 **a**

Shape	Cubes
1	4
2	8
3	12
4	16

b 40

11 **a** 103
b 28

12 **a** 51p
b 60p

13 **a** £5.68
b £12.04

14 **a** £11.85
b £3.36
c £3.06

15 **a** 5
b 3kg
c 22 000g

16 **a** 6.15 p.m.
b 2.55 p.m.
c 19:25

17 **a** 11
b 10
c 12

18 **a** Wednesday at 11 p.m.
b 150 minutes
c –13°C
d $\frac{7}{12}$
e 14 horses and 49 sheep
f £30 and £12

19 **a** 102cm^2
b 1.5, 25.5cm

20 **a** 72
b 4.5